DK Spot the

Bird

Rob Hume

RSPB

LONDON, NEW YORK, MUNICH,
MELBOURNE, AND DELHI

Editor	Lizzie Munsey
Senior Art Editor	Jacqui Swan
Project Art Editor	Duncan Turner
Designer	Fiona Macdonald
Production Editor	Ben Marcus
Production Controller	Erika Pepe
Jacket Editor	Manisha Majithia
Jacket Designer	Mark Cavanagh
Managing Art Editor	Michelle Baxter
Managing Editor	Camilla Hallinan
Publisher	Sarah Larter
Art Director	Philip Ormerod
Associate Publishing Director	Liz Wheeler
Publishing Director	Jonathan Metcalf

First published in 2012 by Dorling Kindersley Limited
80 Strand, London WC2R 0RL
Penguin Group (UK)

2 4 6 8 10 9 7 5 3
001 – 183838 – Apr/2012
Copyright © 2012 Dorling Kindersley Limited

All rights reserved. No part of this publication may be reproduced,
stored in a retrieval system, or transmitted in any form or by any
means, electronic, mechanical, photocopying, recording, or
otherwise, without the prior written permission of the copyright owner.

A CIP catalogue record for this book is available from the British Library
ISBN 978-1-40938-652-0

Printed and bound in China
by South China Printing Company (Ltd)

Discover more at
www.dk.com

Stickers

Once you have seen a bird, find its sticker at
the back of the book and add it to the page.

Seen it!

Seen it!

Contents

**Plus over 100 stickers
at the back**

Icons

♂ This symbol is used to show when a male bird
is pictured, if the female looks different.

Habitat – where
the bird lives

Food – what
the bird eats

Length – from
tail to beak

Where are they?

Birds are almost everywhere, but there are more birds in some places than in others. You will always see more birds near water.

Towns and cities

Some birds are quite happy with urban life. Pigeons are common in towns and cities, and even birds of prey such as Peregrine falcons have been seen nesting on tall buildings in cities.

Gardens

If there is a garden where you live, you can start birdwatching by looking out of the window. You can encourage more birds to come to your garden by giving them food, water, or nest boxes (see pages 12–13).

Rivers and lakes

Wherever they live, birds all need to drink and wash. Some birds can also swim, and many eat insects and other things that live near water. You will always see more birds near water.

Woodland

Many birds live in woods, and leafy summer trees are easy places for birds to hide in. This makes it much harder to see them in the woods. You will probably hear more birds than you see.

Seashore

Some birds only live near the sea, and nest on cliffs. Others walk along the shore in search of food. Look out for waders such as Oystercatchers.

Which bird?

Birds can be hard to tell apart. To help you learn which bird you are looking at, look first at its size, then its shape, then its colour.

Size
If you see a bird you don't know, try to compare it to a bird you do know, starting with its size.

Robin
small

Town Pigeon
medium

Mallard
large

Mute Swan
huge

Shape
Then get an idea of its shape. Look at the length of the tail, the shape of the body, and the type of legs and beak.

Sharp beak

Grey Heron

Short tail

Round body

Long legs

Wren

Colour
Now look at what colour your bird is. Has it got any special pattern or patches of bright colours?

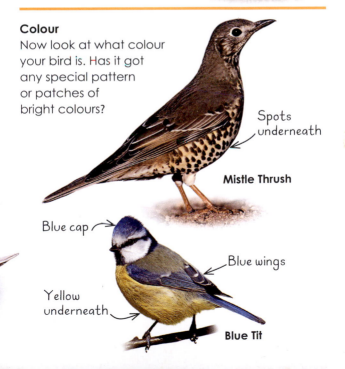

Spots underneath

Mistle Thrush

Blue cap

Blue wings

Yellow underneath

Blue Tit

Behaviour

The way a bird behaves is often because of what it eats and how it gets its food. Watching bird behaviour can help you identify birds.

Dunnock

This bird eats small seeds and grubs from the ground. It shuffles close to the edge of hedges and flowerbeds, trying to stay out of sight of predators.

Heron

Herons eat fish, which they catch with their beaks. You see them standing at the water's edge or paddling slowly and quietly, ready to snatch any fish that swims past.

House Sparrow

Sparrows love to be in noisy little flocks. They squabble and chirrup while they feed next to each other, eating seeds and tiny insects like greenfly.

Strong beak for drilling holes

Short legs and sharp claws for clinging onto the tree

Great Spotted Woodpecker

Woodpeckers are specially suited to living in trees. The Great Spotted Woodpecker makes holes in trees for its nests, and eats insects that it finds in the bark.

Tail is used as prop against the tree

Watch them fly

All European birds can fly. How they fly and the shape of their wings and tail can help you identify them when they are in the air (see also pages 68–69).

Blue Tit
Short dash from perch to perch.

Fluttery wings

Long-tailed Tit
Long, up-and-down swoops.

Very long tail

Sand Martin
Fluttery flight, with regular, even flaps.

Wings point backwards

Long wings

Long wings

Long forked tail

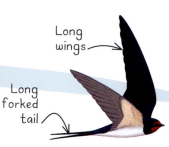

House Martin
Flicks its wings and makes circles in the air.

Swallow
Quick flight, can turn and twist very easily.

Wide round wings

Short round wings

Lapwing
Flies long distances very slowly, so that it doesn't tire itself out.

Song Thrush
Doesn't go far. Flies up from the lawn into the nearest bush.

Buzzard
Flies very high, going round and round for many minutes at a time, looking for prey.

Long wide wings

Notched tail

Chaffinch
Flies quickly, with up-and-down swoops.

Whirring wings

Trailing tail

Pheasant
Flies short distances, very fast and straight.

In the garden

Gardens are great places to see birds. You can encourage more birds to visit your garden by giving them food, water, and somewhere to shelter.

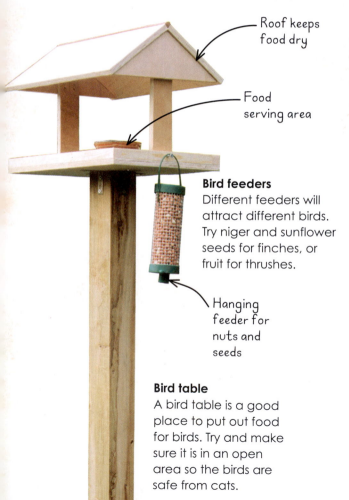

Roof keeps food dry

Food serving area

Bird feeders
Different feeders will attract different birds. Try niger and sunflower seeds for finches, or fruit for thrushes.

Hanging feeder for nuts and seeds

Bird table
A bird table is a good place to put out food for birds. Try and make sure it is in an open area so the birds are safe from cats.

Rose hips

Plants
Some plants will attract more birds than others. Sunflowers are good, but bushes with seeds and berries are best. Lawns are good places for birds to find worms.

Hole for Blue Tits and Sparrows

Open for Robins and Wrens

Bird box
These boxes give birds somewhere to build their nests. They come in many shapes and sizes, which are good for different birds.

Bird bath
A small bird bath gives birds clean water to drink as well as somewhere to wash. They need to wash to keep their feathers clean and healthy.

Useful words

Bar
A plumage mark that crosses a bird's body, wing, or tail.

Beak or bill
The nose and mouth of a bird. It has no teeth and a tough, stiff covering like a fingernail.

Bird of prey
A bird with a hooked beak, which kills and eats other animals.

Call
Each type of bird makes sounds that are different from other birds. Calls are simple notes that help them keep in touch.

Chick
A baby bird, before it can fly.

Conifer
A tree with sharp, needle-like leaves and seeds hidden in cones. Some birds only live in coniferous forests.

Crest
A tuft of feathers on a bird's head that can be lifted up like a fan or spike.

Flock
A group of birds.

Glide
The part of flight where a bird keeps its outstretched wings still between wingbeats.

Immature
A bird that is old enough to be able to fly, but is not yet an adult.

Juvenile
A young bird in its very first plumage.

Migration
A long journey made twice a year, between summer and winter areas.

Moult
The changing of old feathers for new ones. Most birds moult their feathers twice a year.

Plumage
The feathers on a bird's body. Also the pattern on a bird's feathers, which may be different in summer and winter or different for male and female birds.

Predator
An animal that eats other animals.

Prey
An animal that is eaten by other animals.

Roost
To sleep (for a bird). Also a place where birds sleep.

Song
Each kind of bird has its own song, which tells you which bird it is. The song is longer than a call and helps birds to defend areas near the nest. It can also help male birds attract females as mates.

Streak
A plumage mark that runs lengthwise along a bird's body.

Trill
One note that is repeated quickly many times in a row as part of a bird's song or call.

Warble
A bird's song that flows along musically, like a whistle or flute.

Wingbeat
A flap of a bird's wings.

Wingtip
The point or end of the wing: the two wingtips lie alongside the tail when the wings are closed.

Parts of birds

All birds have feathers. These grow in rows and patches and give a bird its colour and patterns. The feathers are moulted once or twice a year. Some birds' plumage changes as they get older, and some birds change from summer to winter colours.

Head

Beak or bill

Wings, which have several rows of big feathers

Breast

Wingtip

Underparts or belly

Leg

Tail

Bright
blue cap

White cheeks
and forehead

Blue wings

Yellow
chest

Blue tail

Flit and bounce
Blue Tits dash about in trees and
hedges. Look for the little blue
cap with a white ring around it.

Blue Tit

These tiny birds love coming to bird
feeders. They often hang upside
down to peck at the food.

Woods,
gardens

Seeds, nuts,
insects

11.5 cm
(4½ in)

Seen it!

Tilt and turn
Great Tits often turn upside down to get to their food. They make loud seesaw noises in spring.

Green back

Shiny black head with big white cheeks

Grey and white wings

Yellow underneath with a black stripe

Great Tit

Great Tits like building their nests in nestboxes. They enjoy sunflower seeds and peanuts from bird feeders.

Woods, gardens

Insects, nuts, berries

14 cm (5½ in)

Seen it!

Black head with white patch

Pale lines across wing

White cheeks and back of neck

Tiny bird
Coal Tits are even smaller than Blue Tits (page 16). They have no blue on them.

Very long tail

Pink back

Black stripes on head

Ball and stick
These tiny birds look like fluffy balls with long tails. They follow each other from place to place.

Coal Tit

Coal Tits will take peanuts from a bird feeder, but then fly away to eat the nuts somewhere safe nearby.

Coniferous woods, gardens

Insects, seeds

11.5 cm (4½ in)

Seen it!

Long-tailed Tit

You might see a Long-tailed Tit carrying a caterpillar to its nest. Birds without their own chicks often help their brothers or sisters feed their families.

Woods, gardens

Insects, seeds, caterpillars

14 cm (5½ in)

Seen it!

Grey band
on cap

Noisy friends
Sparrows love to be together.
They fight and chase each
other around feeders, but
mostly just sit and chirp and
chirrup noisily.

Streaky back

Black
under
chin

♂

Grey underneath

House Sparrow

Sparrows like to nest in holes in
buildings, especially under the roof.
Females are plainer than males.

Towns,
farms

Seeds, berries,
insects

14 cm
(5½ in)

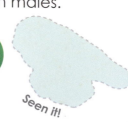

Seen it!

Scratchy and loud
Wrens make harsh, irritable calls and very loud, musical, warbling songs – the whole bird throbs as it sings!

Sharp beak

Bars on back

Short tail often tipped up

Pale underneath

Wren

Wrens hunt for insects and spiders in dark, shady places behind sheds, under hedges, and in ditches.

Gardens, forest

Insects, seeds

10 cm (4 in)

Seen it!

Flit and flash
The perky Robin bobs its head and flits its wings. You often see a flash of orange or hear its warbling song.

Bright orange face and chest

Big black eye

Dumpy brown body

Perky tail

Paler underneath

Droopy wings

Robin

Male Robins sing loudly from a perch to warn other male Robins to keep off their patch. They are not shy!

Woods, gardens

Insects, berries, seeds

14 cm (5½ in)

Seen it!

Streak of gold
Goldfinches fly from
perch to perch,
flashing the yellow
bands on their wings.
They always call to
each other as they fly.

Red, cream,
and black face

Plain brown
back

Yellow band
on wing

Cream
belly

Goldfinch

These birds like nothing better than a
field full of thistles – they eat the soft
seeds from thistle flower heads.

Woods,
gardens

Insects,
seeds

10 cm
(4 in)

Seen it!

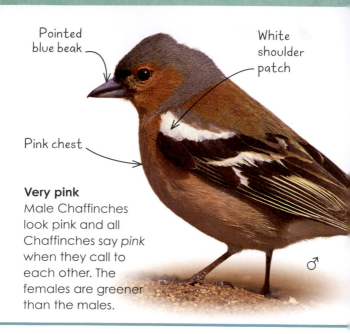

Pointed
blue beak

White
shoulder
patch

Pink chest

Very pink
Male Chaffinches
look pink and all
Chaffinches say *pink*
when they call to
each other. The
females are greener
than the males.

♂

Dark mask
on face

Yellow streak
on wing

Triangular
beak

Seed eater
Greenfinches use
their beaks to
tear open seeds
and rose hips.
They love eating
sunflower seeds
at bird feeders.

Green
body

Chaffinch

These birds feed on the ground under trees, or under feeders, where they pick up food spilled by other birds.

Seen it!

Woods, gardens

Insects, seeds

14.5 cm (5¾ in)

Greenfinch

In spring, Greenfinches sing a lot, from treetops and in the air. When they fly, they flutter their wings quickly, like big bats.

Seen it!

Woods, hedges

Seeds, berries, nuts

15 cm (6 in)

Black and yellow wings

Black cap

Seen it!

Siskin

These little birds love to eat sunflower or niger seeds from bird feeders.

♂

Grey collar

Dunnock

These birds stay close to flowerbeds. They creep and hop quietly on the ground, or sit in bushes.

Streaky brown feathers

Seen it!

Black cap and beak

Grey back

Bullfinch

Bullfinches are shy, quiet birds that live in hedges and low bushes. They eat buds and seeds.

Pink chest

♂

White around tail

Seen it!

Grey head

Brown back

Seen it!

Linnet
Flocks of lively, twittering Linnets are found among short weeds or in places without many plants.

Streaky wings and tail

♂

Yellow head

Rusty brown back

Yellowhammer
Yellowhammers sing from the tops of bushes or hedges. Their bright heads catch the sunlight.

Seen it!

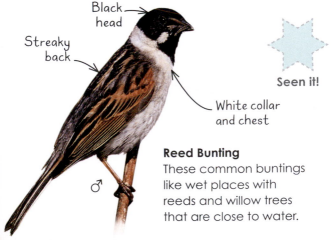

Black head

Streaky back

Seen it!

White collar and chest

Reed Bunting
These common buntings like wet places with reeds and willow trees that are close to water.

♂

Snail smasher
Song Thrushes catch snails and then noisily smash the snails' shells against stones.

Plain brown back

Yellow on beak

V-shaped spots underneath

Pale legs

Dark beak

Grey back

Berry eater
Mistle Thrushes like eating berries, especially from Mountain Ash trees.

Pale lines on wings

Round spots underneath

White sides on tail

Song Thrush

Thrushes have beautiful songs, with each part of the song repeated two or three times.

Woods, farms, gardens

Worms, snails, fruit

23 cm
(9 in)

Seen it!

Mistle Thrush

Mistle Thrushes guard their nests and may attack if a predator threatens the nest. The rest of the time they are shy and easily scared away.

Farms, gardens

Worms, seeds, berries

27 cm
(10½ in)

Seen it!

Bright yellow beak

Beautiful song
Male Blackbirds like this one sing loud, warbling songs from trees and rooftops. Female Blackbirds are dark brown.

All-black feathers

♂

Long tail often tilted upwards

Blackbird

Blackbirds run and hop on a lawn, then stop to look around. They often tug up worms.

Woods, gardens

Worms, berries insects

25 cm (10 in)

Seen it!

Loud bird

Starlings walk along, then lean forward to peck at the ground. They squabble noisily over grubs and crumbs.

Spiky beak

Shiny black, purple, and green feathers

Strong red-brown legs and feet

Short square tail

Starling

These birds form big flocks and sleep in woods and reedbeds. Sometimes more than a million flock together.

Woods, gardens

Insects, seeds, berries

21 cm (8 in)

Seen it!

White patch on shoulder

Black head and chest

White underneath

Chatterboxes
Magpies catch insects and look for scraps, all the time chattering to each other with fast, rattling calls.

Three coos
Collared Doves always sing three coos, like *cu-cooo-cuk!* They like to sit on roofs and aerials.

Round dark red eye

Pale fawn body

Black wingtips

Black collar

Short red legs

Magpie

In spring, Magpies gather in the treetops to sleep, in groups of around 10 or 20 or even more. They eat other birds' eggs.

Farms, woods, towns

Insects, eggs, grain, scraps

Long tail

Seen it!

45 cm (18 in)

Collared Dove

Other pigeons are silent when they fly, but the Collared Dove makes whirring calls. Look out for the black collar on its neck.

Gardens, farms

Grain, seeds, buds

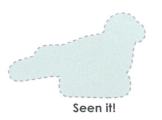

Seen it!

32 cm (12½ in)

Many colours
Pigeons come in different colours, but you can still recognize them from their shape and size.

Short beak

Blue, black, white, or brown feathers

Shiny green and purple neck

Pink feet

White on neck

Noisy fliers
Woodpigeons clap their wings and make a clattering noise with them when they fly off.

White on wing

Pink chest

Town Pigeon

Pigeons are found almost everywhere, including towns and cities. They eat nearly anything and meet in large flocks.

Cities, farms, cliffs, towns

Seeds, berries, insects

33 cm
(13 in)

Seen it!

Woodpigeon

Woodpigeons are bigger than Town Pigeons and often fly in big flocks. You can see white patches on their wings when they fly.

Woods, farms

Buds, berries, fruit

41 cm
(16 in)

Seen it!

Black and white tail

Tiniest bird

This is Europe's smallest bird. Look for the black and yellow streak on its head as it flits about in dense bushes and trees.

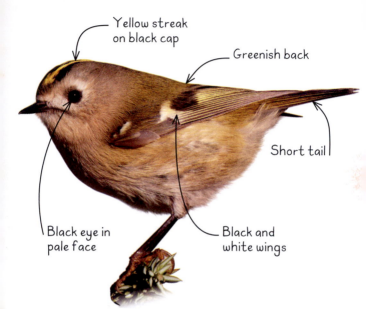

Yellow streak on black cap

Greenish back

Short tail

Black eye in pale face

Black and white wings

Goldcrest

A Goldcrest's nest is a tiny ball of feathers, moss, and lichens, hanging under the branch of a pine tree.

Woods

Insects, spiders

9 cm (3½ in)

Seen it!

Busy tail
Pied Wagtails always wag their tails up and down. The females are greyer than the males.

White face

Black bib

Black and white tail

♂

White underneath

Pied Wagtail

Pied Wagtails like water of all sorts, but are just as likely to be found on roofs, footpaths, and in car parks.

Watersides, towns

Insects, seeds

18 cm (7 in)

Seen it!

Grey back

Very long thin tail

Seen it!

Yellow under tail

Grey Wagtail
This slim wagtail is always near water. It likes streams but even a puddle on a roof will do.

Yellow underneath

Green back

Seen it!

Black legs

Yellow Wagtail
Watch for this summer bird around cows and horses in grassy fields near rivers and pools.

Meadow Pipit
This pipit likes moors and heaths in summer but comes down to fields in winter, especially near the sea.

Thin beak

Streaky brown back

Thin orange legs

Seen it!

Redwing

Small flocks of these dark thrushes visit from October to April. They feed in fields and hedges.

Pale stripe over eye

Red under wing

Streaks underneath

Seen it!

Grey head

Spotted chest

Grey above black tail

Seen it!

Fieldfare

Flocks of Fieldfares often mix with Redwings in winter. They make loud, chuckling calls as they fly.

Brown back

Sand Martin

These martins visit in the summer, and use their tiny beaks and feet to scrape tunnels out of sandy cliffs.

Long wings

White underneath

Seen it!

Forked tail

Tiny beak

Nearly all black

Paler chin

Notched tail

Stiff curved wings

Screaming parties
Watch for Swifts catching flies high in the sky. They dash round and round the rooftops making loud, screeching screams.

Swift

Swifts never perch – they always fly. Look for them in summer – by August, they will be on their way to Africa.

Towns, cliffs

Insects

16 cm (6½ in)

Seen it!

Red throat

Dark blue back

Long forked tail

Pale underneath

Nearby nesters

Swallows nest in sheds and barns, and often sit and sing on an aerial or wire. Look out for their long tails. They visit Europe in large flocks in the summer.

Swallow

Swallows do their hunting in the air, catching big flies in their very wide mouths.

Villages, hedges

Insects

18 cm (7 in)

Seen it!

High fliers

House Martins fly high up in the sky to catch flies, but also collect mud from puddles to make their nests. They only visit Europe in the summer.

Black back

Long dark tail

White underneath

Feathered legs

House Martin

These birds build mud nests under the gutters. If you are lucky, you can watch them nesting under the roof.

Towns, mountains

Insects, spiders

12 cm (4¾ in)

Seen it!

Winter groups

In winter, Skylarks gather in flocks in open fields to look for food. They hardly ever perch in trees.

Crest

Streaks on face

Streaky brown back

White underneath

Skylark

This bird has a special song, which it performs while flying up into the air as if pulled on a string.

Moors, farms

Seeds, grain, insects

18 cm (7 in)

Seen it!

Bird groups

Some birds live on their own, but others stay together. Some live in families in the summer but meet in big flocks in the winter.

Winter group
Flocks of Blue, Great, and Long-tailed tits wander through the treetops in autumn and winter, in groups of 20, 30, or even 50.

Long journey
Some birds meet in huge flocks and migrate long distances for the winter. Pink-footed Geese fly thousands of kilometres every year (see pages 102–103).

Each bird
follows the
leader

V shapes

When they fly, geese and other birds such as gulls and cranes fly in long lines or V shapes. This helps them keep in touch with each other. It might also be easier to fly through the air just behind and to one side of another bird.

Huge flock

Starlings feed in small flocks but on winter evenings they get together in flocks of tens or hundreds of thousands. The whole flock then sleeps together in a wood or reed bed.

Thin beak

Black cap

Plain brown back

Grey chin

Blackcap
Male Blackcaps have black caps but females have brown ones. Listen for their fast, warbling songs.

Grey underneath

♂

Seen it!

Wheatear
If a Wheatear flies away from you, you can see a white patch above its tail, which looks like an upside-down black T.

Black mask
Grey back

Black wings

♂

Black tail tip

Seen it!

White neck patch

Black head

Red-brown chest

♂

Seen it!

Stonechat
The best place to spot these is a heath with lots of gorse bushes – they perch right on top.

Dull green back

Spindly black legs

Seen it!

Chiffchaff
Chiffchaffs sing *chiff-chaff-chiff-chaff-chaff-chaff-chiff* all day. Look for them in bushes and treetops.

Willow Warbler
This green and cream warbler has a lovely, sweet, rippling song.

Greenish back

Cream underneath

Pale brown legs

Seen it!

Pale stripe over eye

Streaky back

Seen it!

Pale underneath

Sedge Warbler
Look for these birds in summer, in reeds and willow trees or thorn bushes close to the water's edge.

Red patch
on head

Cream
underneath

White
shoulder
patch

Black and
white back

White spots
on wings

Spring drumming
In the spring,
woodpeckers make
drum roll noises by
hammering their
beaks against trees
– they may be easier
to hear than to see.

Bright red
under tail

Great Spotted Woodpecker

Woodpeckers chip bits of wood from trees to look for grubs, but they also visit bird tables.

Woods,
gardens

Insects,
seeds, nuts

22 cm
(9 in)

Seen it!

Spiky beak

Red cap

Green back

Flashing yellow
These birds are
usually seen flying
up from the grass,
flashing a patch of
yellow over the tail.
They make loud
laughing sounds.

Yellow
near tail

Green Woodpecker

Green Woodpeckers use their long, sticky tongues to pull ants out of their underground tunnels.

21·3·14
Kew

Woods,
gardens

Ants

32 cm
(12½ in)

Seen it!

Long claws

Curved beak

Streaky
brown back

Silky white
underneath

Spiky tail

Up and down
Treecreepers always
creep up trees, flat to
the bark, resting on
their stiff tails. Then
they fly to the bottom
of the next tree and
start again.

Treecreeper

Treecreepers are brilliant at climbing
trees but can hardly stand at
all on flat ground.

Woods

Insects,
spiders

12.5 cm
(5 in)

Seen it!

Whistle and hop
Nuthatches hop about on trees and on the ground underneath. Listen for their loud whistles and trills.

Short black and white tail

Grey back

Black eye stripe

Orange underneath

Nuthatch

Nuthatches nest in holes. They use sticky mud to make the entrance to the hole just the right size.

Woods, gardens

Seeds, berries, nuts

12.5 cm (5 in)

Seen it!

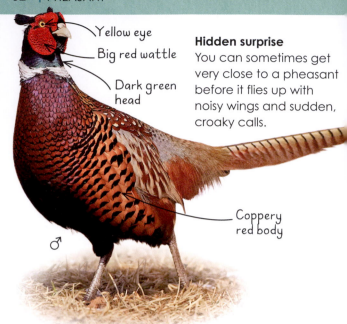

Yellow eye

Big red wattle

Dark green head

Coppery red body

♂

Hidden surprise
You can sometimes get very close to a pheasant before it flies up with noisy wings and sudden, croaky calls.

White skin around beak

Black body

Listen out
Rooks make many loud *caw caw* sounds, especially around their nests.

Purple shine

Feathers on legs look like baggy trousers

Long pointed tail

Seen it!

Fields, woods

Seeds, berries, insects

Pheasant

Pheasants spend most of their time in woods but also visit open fields and roadsides when they need to find food.

70 cm
(28 in)

Rook

Rooks like to be together. They build big stick nests close together in the tops of trees – the groups of nests can be quite easy to see.

Farms, gardens

Worms, seeds, roots

Seen it!

45 cm
(18 in)

Not picky

Crows poke their beaks into anything that they think they can eat, including dead animals and other birds' eggs. They make loud *caw* noises.

Strong black beak

Smooth black body

Thick legs and feet

Carrion Crow

You will see crows almost anywhere, from towns to the countryside, and even on the beach.

Farms, towns

Insects, eggs, grain

48 cm (19 in)

Seen it!

Different places

Hooded Crows are found in different areas to Carrion Crows. Look for them in Scotland, Ireland, and the Isle of Man.

Heavy beak

Black head and chest

Black wings

Grey body

Hooded Crow

Hooded Crows look a bit different but behave just like Carrion Crows. They love to eat food from rubbish tips.

Farms, towns

Insects, eggs, grain

48 cm (19 in)

Seen it!

Breeding

Different types of birds have different ways of pairing with a mate, nesting, and then rearing their chicks. However, there are some things that most birds do in the same way.

Singing
The male bird often sings in spring and summer to try to attract a female. Singing also tells other males to keep away. Blackbirds sing beautiful, musical songs.

Pairing
Most birds make pairs – a male and a female. The pair find a good place to make a nest, and keep other birds away from it. Pairs of grebes dance together on the water.

Nesting

Most birds make nests. The nest is not a home – it is a safe place for the female to lay her eggs. Nests are often made of grass and twigs, but storks make theirs from sticks.

Sitting

Sometimes it is the female that sits on the eggs until they hatch. For other birds, like this swan, both parents take turns sitting on the eggs.

Feeding chicks

The parents bring food to the chicks in the nest. Blue Tit chicks will leave the nest after about two weeks.

Noisy Jack

Jackdaws are named after their calls: loud, sharp *jack* sounds. They eat anything they can find.

Black face

White eye

Grey neck

Black bib

Dull black body

Jackdaw

Jackdaws like to feed in fields with Rooks (page 53). They also like big lawns and parks.

Fields, parks

Worms, seeds, berries

33 cm (13 in)

Seen it!

Giant acrobat

Ravens are the biggest crows in the world. They are experts at acrobatics in the air, and can even fly upside down.

Huge beak

Long wings

All black

Long diamond-shaped tail

Raven

Ravens like big, open spaces, near cliffs and in hills. They sometimes nest on big buildings.

Cliffs, hills

Birds, insects, grain

60 cm (24 in)

Seen it!

Black moustache

Seen it!

Blue patch on wing

Pinkish brown body

White under tail

Small curved beak

Grey back

Bars underneath

Wedge-shaped tail

Jay

Look for Jays in autumn, when they fly overhead with their mouths full of acorns, which they bury to eat later. Jays also eat other birds' eggs.

Woods, gardens

Insects, eggs, acorns

34 cm (13½ in)

Shy but loud
Jays are shy and fly off with a loud screech if you get too close.

Cuckoo

Female Cuckoos lay their eggs in other birds' nests – the other bird then looks after the Cuckoo chick.

Woods, farms

Caterpillars, insects

33 cm (13 in)

Mystery voice
Cuckoos sing *cuc-koo* but are hard to spot. Look for one on a tall tree or wire in spring.

Seen it!

Grey head

Big dark eye

Short hooked beak

Bright yellow feet

♂

Hover and dive
Kestrels can hover over one spot, as if on a string. They dive down to catch mice and voles.

Spotted red-brown back

Kestrel

Kestrels perch near roads, so you can sometimes get a close look. The female is browner than the male.

Woods, farms

Voles, lizards, worms

35 cm (14 in)

Seen it!

Black hood

White neck

Dark streaks underneath

Turning and twisting
Hobbies glide and twist, using their feet to catch insects and small birds in the air.

Red under tail

Hobby

This small falcon finds most of its food near water. Look for it in summer, near lakes and flooded gravel pits.

Watersides, woods

Small birds, insects

30 cm (12 in)

Seen it!

Quick plunge
Peregrines are famous for making fast dives to catch small birds in flight.

Black hood

Pale cheek

Thick hooked beak

Bars underneath

Strong yellow feet

Peregrine

These birds like to nest high up. They used to nest in mountains and on cliffs, but now use high buildings.

Woods, farms

Small birds

36 cm (14 in)

Seen it!

Hooked beak

Brown body

Pale U shape on chest

Spotted brown underneath

Float and glide
Buzzards fly on long, broad wings. They drift and float in circles high in the sky, making loud mewing sounds.

Wide tail with dark bands

Buzzard

Buzzards spend hours spiralling round in the sky, showing off to each other and looking for small animals to eat.

Hills, woods, farms

Small animals

55 cm (21 in)

Seen it!

Pale eye

Grey-brown above

Short wings

Barred below

Thin yellow legs

Dash and grab
Sparrowhawks fly low and fast. They catch small birds close to the ground.

Sparrowhawk

These birds will visit garden bird feeders, but to eat the other birds, not the food you put out.

Woods, valleys

Small birds

35 cm (14 in)

Seen it!

Streaked
white head

Very long
wings

Red-brown
body

Forked tail

Elegant glider
Kites glide on their long, bent
wings. They twist their long,
forked tails to help them
steer in the air.

Red Kite

You can see kites where there are
woods and trees scattered over
farmland, especially in hilly places.

Woods,
valleys

Dead
animals

60 cm
(23½ in)

Seen it!

Flight styles

Birds do not all fly in the same way. Every bird has a flight pattern, which is different depending on how often it flaps its wings or holds them still to glide along.

Finch
Finches fly in sets of short, fast bursts of wingbeats between rolling glides.

Swallow
Swallows fly sideways and swoop, with bursts of smooth wingbeats between glides.

Woodpecker

Woodpeckers make fast bursts of
wingbeats, then rise up before
closing their wings to make deep
downward swoops.

Duck

Ducks beat their wings fast and steadily,
and only glide when they come down
to land on land or water.

Big black eyes

Large round head

What a hoot
The best way to find this bird is to listen for it. It hoots and makes sharp *tu-wit* noises.

Red-brown or grey body

Short barred tail

Tawny Owl

These owls only come out at night. Sometimes you may see one resting against a tree trunk.

Woods

Mice, frogs, worms

38 cm (15 in)

seen it!

Big head

Black eyes

Heart-shaped face

White underneath

Night hunter
Barn Owls usually only come out at night, except in mid-summer and on very cold, icy winter days.

Barn Owl

Barn Owls like to nest in old buildings and hollow trees. They hunt over grassy places, often near roads.

Farms, marshes

Mice, rats, birds

35 cm (14 in)

Seen it!

Dark green head

Yellow beak

♂

Common duck
Look for Mallards anywhere near water. They are quite happy even on a small duckpond or by a stream.

Brown body

Pale eye

Brown head

Mudlarks
Teals like paddling in wet mud and shallow water. They use their flat beaks to find tiny seeds and other food.

Grey beak

White line on wing

♂

Grey legs

Green band on wing

Mallard

Some Mallards are quite tame and come to feed on park lakes. Female Mallards are streaky brown all over.

Black and white tail

Watersides

Insects, seeds, roots

60 cm (24 in)

Seen it!

Teal

This is our smallest duck. Flocks of Teals like grassy and muddy places near lakes and by the sea. Sometimes they meet in flocks of hundreds.

Marshes, small pools

Plants, seeds

36 cm (14 in)

Seen it!

Gadwall

These ducks have orange legs like Mallards, but with plain brown heads and dark grey bodies.

Grey body

Black beak

♂

Seen it!

Shoveler

These unusual looking ducks use their long beaks to search for food under water.

Green head

♂

Seen it!

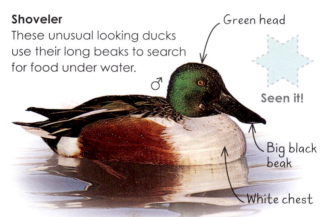

Big black beak

White chest

White face spot

Black head with golden eye

♂

Goldeneye

These diving ducks go under the water for a long time. They are often under water.

Bright white body

Seen it!

Wigeon

Colourful Wigeons feed close together in flocks on short grass, or swim out on the water.

Brown head

Seen it!

Short blue beak

Black and white near tail

♂

Seen it!

Tufted Duck

To identify this diving duck, look for the wavy tuft on the back of its head.

Black head

♂

Black back

White sides

Pochard

Pochards often mix with Tufted Ducks. They sleep in the daytime and feed after dark.

Red head

♂

Grey body

Black tail

Seen it!

Strong beak
Eiders use their long, thick beaks for pulling mussels off rocks and crushing the shells to get at the soft shellfish inside.

White back

Black cap

Long beak

Black belly

Shining white
This big duck waddles like a goose. Parts of it are bright white and easy to see on mud or a marsh by the sea.

Bright red beak

Black head

Broad orange band

White body

Pink legs

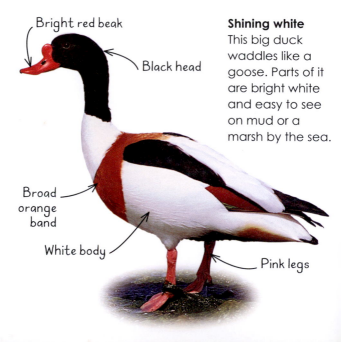

Eider

These ducks only live on the sea, not on fresh water. You can sometimes see them quite close up around seaweed and rocky islands. Female Eiders are brown.

Coasts

Crabs,
shellfish

62 cm
(24½ in)

Seen it!

Shelduck

Shelducks live on the coast, but also nest inland, often near flooded gravel pits. Look for them on grassy banks.

Coasts

Algae,
snails

60 cm
(24 in)

Seen it!

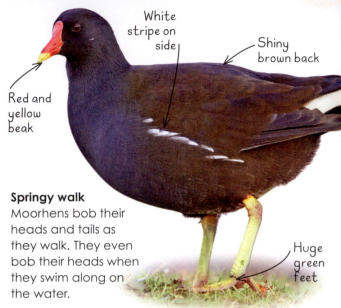

White stripe on side

Shiny brown back

Red and yellow beak

Springy walk
Moorhens bob their heads and tails as they walk. They even bob their heads when they swim along on the water.

Huge green feet

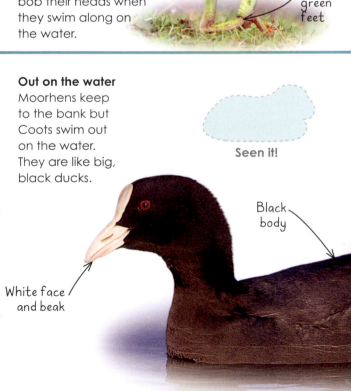

Out on the water
Moorhens keep to the bank but Coots swim out on the water. They are like big, black ducks.

Seen it!

Black body

White face and beak

Moorhen

Any wet place except the seaside is good for Moorhens, especially if there are reeds or tussocks of long grass to hide in.

Ponds, rivers

Seeds, fruit, snails, insects

33 cm (13 in)

Seen it!

Coot

Look for Coots on lakes and ponds in parks. In some places they are very tame.

Lakes

Seeds, snails, grass

37 cm (14½ in)

Round tail

Sharp pointed beak

Black crest

Red-brown ruff

White neck

Sleek and slender
Great Crested Grebes have long, gleaming white necks. They may be stretched up straight or curled down into the shoulders.

Seen it!

Seen it!

Round head

Red cheeks

Pale spot near beak

Bobbing along
Little Grebes are tiny, round birds. They often dive under water, then bob up again nearby.

Great Crested Grebe

Grebes dive for fish in lakes or on the sea. You can see them all year round.

Lakes, rivers, sea

Fish

Brown body

Short rounded tail

50 cm (19 in)

Little Grebe

These are the smallest swimming birds on British lakes. Listen for their shrill, trilling calls across the water.

Lakes, rivers

Fish, molluscs

Round fluffy body

Tiny tail

27 cm (11 in)

Feeding

Food provides energy for all birds. Some of the biggest birds can go for days without food. Some small birds must eat almost as much as they weigh, every day.

Curlew

Long thin beak →

Beaks

Birds' beaks give you clues about what they eat. Chaffinches use their beaks to split seeds. Curlews use theirs to push into mud and pull out worms. Buzzards tear their prey apart.

Triangular beak

Short hooked beak

Buzzard

Chaffinch

Strong stomach

Grebes swallow some of their own feathers. These line their stomachs and stop sharp fish bones from poking through.

Feet

Birds' legs and feet show how they get to their food. Curlews wade in water. Woodpeckers hang onto branches and tree trunks, and Kestrels use their claws to catch the small animals they eat.

Strong feet

Great Spotted Woodpecker

Curved claws

Curlew

Long legs

Long toes

Kestrel

Dabbling ducks

Some ducks put their heads under water, then suck in a mouthful of water. They then push the water out with their tongues, keeping any seeds behind in their mouths.

Black head and neck

White
chinstrap

Noisy bird
This is our biggest
goose, with a deep
honking voice.
Canada Geese are
almost always in flocks.

Grey-brown
body

Black legs

White
around
tail

Canada Goose

Look for these geese on grassy
places by lakes, or on stony islands.
They often mix with Greylag Geese.

Rivers,
grassland

Grass, grain,
plants

1 m
(3 ft)

Seen it!

Plain brown head

Big orange beak

Flocking together
Greylags are common
geese. They are a paler
brown than Canada
Geese and often mix
with them.

White bars on grey-brown body

White around tail

Pink feet

Greylag Goose

Greylags usually stay in large flocks,
and are very noisy when they all
fly off together.

Marshes,
pastures

Grass, roots,
grain

80 cm
(31½ in)

Seen it!

Pink-footed Goose

Tens of thousands of these wild geese come south to parts of England and Scotland each winter.

Dark brown head

Pink band on beak

Pink feet

Seen it!

Brent Goose

Thousands of these dumpy geese come to the coast each winter. They breed in the Arctic in the summer. Sometimes they are quite tame.

Black head

White around tail

Black chest

Black legs

Seen it!

Bewick's Swan

These swans visit in big flocks each winter. They often mix together with other swans.

Seen it!

Round yellow patch on beak

All-white feathers

Whooper Swan

This is bigger than the Bewick's Swan. You can see both of these swans together in the winter.

Pointed yellow patch on beak

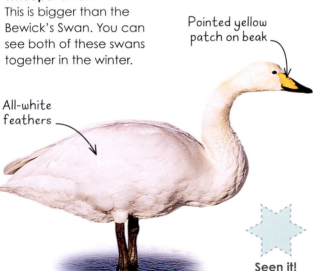

All-white feathers

Seen it!

Snake necks

Swans have long necks that can curl into an S shape. They plunge their heads under water to feed, but can also feed on dry land.

Black knob above beak

Orange beak

All-white feathers

Mute Swan

These swans make big nests of grass and reed stems close to water. They chase anyone who gets too close.

Lakes, rivers

Plants

1.5 m (5 ft)

Seen it!

Striped head
Look at a heron and you should see a white head with a long, black stripe, which goes back into a thin, pointed crest.

Crest

Dagger beak

Snaky neck

Grey back

White underneath

Long legs

Grey Heron

Herons are very patient fishermen. They wade or stand still in water until they can snatch a small fish.

Watersides

Fish, frogs, rats

95 cm (37 in)

Seen it!

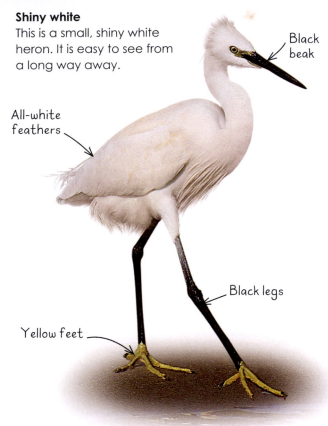

Shiny white
This is a small, shiny white heron. It is easy to see from a long way away.

Black beak

All-white feathers

Black legs

Yellow feet

Little Egret

Little Egrets are most common by the sea. They feed by rivers, marshes, and in muddy creeks.

Watersides

Fish, frogs, snails

60 cm (24 in)

Seen it!

European bird
These birds are not found in the British Isles. They are so big you can see them from the train or car.

Red beak

White head and neck

Black wings

Red legs

White Stork

These long-legged birds make giant, messy nests high up on chimneys and telegraph poles.

Rivers, towns

Insects, frogs, fish

1 m (3 ft)

seen it!

Heard not seen
You often hear a Kingfisher before you
see it. It makes a "plop" as it dives and
has a sharp, thin whistle when it flies.

Green-
blue cap

Brilliant
blue back

Dagger
beak

Orange-brown
underneath

Tiny red feet

Kingfisher

Despite their bright colours, these
small birds are hard to see. They sit
quietly in the shade of a leafy bank.

Watersides

Fish, frogs,
insects

16 cm
(6½ in)

Seen it!

Hooked beak

Yellow around beak

White throat

Black body

Smooth divers
Cormorants swim along very low in the water, then gently roll over and dive down to catch fish.

Big black feet

Long tail

Cormorant

You often see a Cormorant standing with its wings spread open, as if hanging them out to dry.

Coast, inland

Fish

90 cm (35 in)

Seen it!

Brown head goes white in winter

Pale grey on top

Bright red beak

Squabbles and squeals
Black-headed Gulls are smaller than other gulls. They make lots of whining and squealing noises.

White body

Red legs

Pale eye

Red spot on big yellow beak

Silvery grey back

Many colours
Herring Gulls come in all shades of brown and grey. They take four years to get their adult colours like this bird.

Pink legs

Seen it!

Black-headed Gull

Gulls often come close to people if they think they can snatch a beakful of food.

Black wingtips

Seen it!

Coasts, inland

Worms, seeds, insects

35 cm (14 in)

Herring Gull

This is the noisy, common seagull at the beach. It might try to steal your lunch!

Black and white wingtips

Coasts, inland

Fish, insects, scraps

60 cm (24 in)

Lesser Black-backed Gull

This is like a dark Herring Gull
(page 94) but with yellow legs
instead of pink. You will see it
by the sea and inland.

Dark grey
back

Yellow
legs

Seen it!

Great Black-backed Gull

This is the biggest gull in the
world. It is usually much less
common than the Herring or
Lesser Black-backed gulls.

Black
back

Pink
legs

Seen it!

Common Gull

This is like a little Herring Gull
but with different colours
on the beak and feet. It
likes to look for worms on
short grass.

Greenish
beak

Dark
eye

Yellow-green
legs

Seen it!

Fulmar

These birds can't stand up. They sit on their nests on cliffs, or fly over the sea on stiff, straight wings.

Seen it!

Big white head

Grey wings and tail

Thick beak

Kittiwake

These gulls nest on cliffs and live out at sea. They can't walk very well and don't join other gulls on fields or the beach.

Dark eye

Black wingtips

Black feet

Seen it!

Guillemot

Look for these on cliff ledges in summer. At other times they live out on the open sea.

Sharp beak

Brown back

Square tail

Seen it!

Black cap

Grey back

Red beak with black tip

Short red legs

Long forked tail

Summer visitor
You can see Common Terns in the summer, by the sea or over lakes in river valleys inland.

Black cap

Black beak

Black legs

Forked tail

Gleaming white
This is the biggest and the palest of our terns. It dives with a big splash, even into very rough seas!

Common Tern

These terns dive into the sea for fish. On lakes, they fly down to the water to catch insects or tiny fish.

Coasts, rivers

Fish, insects

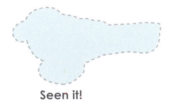

Seen it!

33 cm (13 in)

Sandwich Tern

Sandwich Terns nest on sandy and stony beaches by the sea. You will see them fishing close to the beach.

Coasts, islands

Fish

Seen it!

38 cm (15 in)

Yellow head

Dagger beak

Picky nester
Look for Gannets fishing far out at sea. Thousands nest together on the same cliffs and islands every year.

Long narrow wings

Brilliant white feathers

Black wingtips

Gannet

Gannets eat fish, which they catch at sea. You might see one dive like an arrow, with a big, white splash.

Rocky islands

Fish

87 cm
(34½ in)

Seen it!

Triangular beak

White cheeks

White belly

Waddle and whirr
On land, Puffins waddle about on steep grass slopes near cliffs, but they fly over the sea with fast, whirring wings.

Black back

Bright orange legs

Puffin

Puffins nest on the same cliffs and islands every year. They spend most of their lives out at sea.

FARM ISLANDS
April 2017 & 2012

Coasts, islands

Fish, squid

28 cm (11 in)

seen it!

Migration

Some birds stay in the same place all year. Others go to different places at different times of the year – this is called migration. Usually, migrating birds move from north to south for the winter, when food becomes harder to find in northern areas.

ARCTIC OCEAN

NORTH AMERICA

EUROPE

Arctic Terns fly north to breed

EQUATOR

SOUTH AMERICA

World tour
Arctic Terns make one of the longest migrations. The yearly round trip is more than 40,000 kilometres (25,000 miles).

Icy trip

Migration takes Arctic Terns through many different habitats. However, they spend most of their time flying over the sea. The places terns breed in and spend the winter in are very cold.

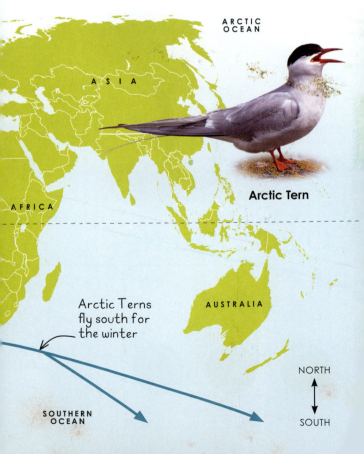

ARCTIC OCEAN

ASIA

AFRICA

Arctic Tern

Arctic Terns fly south for the winter

AUSTRALIA

SOUTHERN OCEAN

NORTH

SOUTH

Clever beak
The Oystercatcher eats shellfish. It slides its beak into the shell to cut it open, or hammers the shell until it breaks.

Long orange beak

Shiny black back

Bright white underneath

Thick pink legs

Oystercatcher

Most Oystercatchers live in flocks by the sea, but you might see some in fields inland or by rivers and lakes.

Beaches, watersides

Worms, molluscs

42 cm (17 in)

Seen it!

Winter bird
Look for flocks of Lapwings resting in wet or ploughed fields in the autumn and winter.

Black cap and crest

Purple patch on shoulder

Big black and white wings

Dark red legs

White underneath

Lapwing

These birds are often called peewits, because that is what their call sounds like – *peewit!*

Farms, watersides

Insects, worms

29 cm (11 in)

Seen it!

Short beak

Black mask

Black ring round chest

Brown back

White belly

Orange legs

Stop and start
Plovers run a bit, stop, tilt down to pick up food, then run again. They meet up in large, tight flocks in winter.

Ringed Plover

You will find Ringed Plovers by water, especially on sandy and muddy beaches at the seaside.

Beaches

Insects, worms

18 cm (7 in)

Seen it!

Mud lover

Look for Curlews on mud and marshland close to the sea. They use their long beaks to probe for food in mud or under water.

Streaky brown feathers

Pale belly

Dull legs

Very long and curved beak

Curlew

The Curlew is named from its loud, ringing call – *curlew*. It also has a beautiful, bubbling song.

Shores, watersides

Insects, molluscs

55 cm (22 in)

Seen it!

Redshank

This bird has big white stripes on its wings that can be seen when it flies. It has loud, ringing calls.

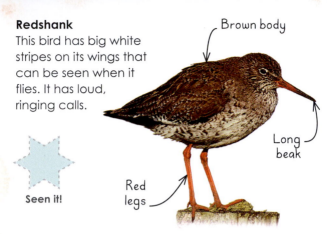

Brown body

Long beak

Red legs

Seen it!

Dunlin

These waders live on mud and sand by the sea. They use their beaks to find food in the mud. In the summer, their bellies turn black.

Thin curved beak

Brown back

Streaked belly

Very dark legs

Seen it!

Turnstone

These birds are found on the beach by the sea. They turn over stones and seaweed to find food.

Short thick beak

Black chest

Bright orange legs

Seen it!

Sanderling

These birds run very fast on sandy beaches. They trot in and out with the waves, looking for food.

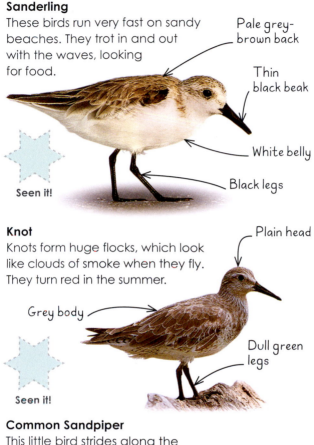

Pale grey-brown back

Thin black beak

White belly

Black legs

Seen it!

Knot

Knots form huge flocks, which look like clouds of smoke when they fly. They turn red in the summer.

Plain head

Grey body

Dull green legs

Seen it!

Common Sandpiper

This little bird strides along the shore, bobbing its head and swinging its tail as it goes.

Brown back

White patch near shoulder

White underneath

Seen it!

Index

Acknowledgments

Dorling Kindersley would like to thank: RSPB consultant Mark Boyd, Liz Moore for picture research, Ann Kay for proofreading, Clare McLean for sticker advice, CTS Peter Pawsey, Claire Bowers for DK images, Jacket Design Development Manager Sophia Tampakopoulos, and Jonny Burrows for design assistance.

The publisher would also like to thank the following for their kind permission to reproduce their photographs:
(Key: a-above; b-below/bottom; c-centre; f-far; l-left; r-right; t-top)
2 Dorling Kindersley: Chris Gomersall Photography (bc). 4 Alamy Images: Pick and Mix Images (bl). Getty Images: Tim Graham (c). 5 Alamy Images: blickwinkel (tr). 7 Dorling Kindersley: Steve Young (cla). 8 Alamy Images: Ray Wilson (cra). Getty Images: Blackpool College (bc). 9 Corbis: Tero Niemi / Naturbild (tr). Dorling Kindersley: Jari Peltomaki (br). 13 Dorling Kindersley: Natural History Museum, London (cl). 21 Dorling Kindersley: Steve Young (ca). 34 Dorling Kindersley: Roger Tidman (cb). 41 Dorling Kindersley: Brian E. Small (ca). 43 Dorling Kindersley: Mike Lane (ca). 46 Dorling Kindersley: Roger Tidman (tl). 47 Dorling Kindersley: Chris Gomersall Photography (cb). 48 Dorling Kindersley: Jari Peltomaki (ca). 56 Getty Images: Tim Oram (cl); Konrad Wothe (br). 57 Getty Images: Tim Graham (c); Joseph Van Os (tl); Ian Grainger (br). 59 Dorling Kindersley: Mike Lane (ca). 67 Alamy Images: Juniors Bildarchiv (ca). 68 Corbis: Roger Tidman (br). 69 Getty Images: Guy Edwardes (c). 71 Dorling Kindersley: Mark Hamblin (ca). 74 Dorling Kindersley: Arundel Wildfowl Trust, West Sussex (cb). 82 Getty Images: David Courtenay (bl). 83 Dorling Kindersley: The National Birds of Prey Centre, Gloucestershire (cl); Jari Peltomaki (tr). Getty Images: S.J. Krasemann (br). 85 Dorling Kindersley: Windrush Photos / David Tipling (ca). 89 Dorling Kindersley: Roger Tidman (cr). 90 Dorling Kindersley: David Cottridge (ca). 91 Dorling Kindersley: White Stork Ciconia ciconia Adult (ca). 92 Corbis: Joe Petersburger / National Geographic Society (ca). 94-95 Dorling Kindersley: Chris Gomersall Photography (ca). 96 Dorling Kindersley: David Tipling Photo Library (c). 97 Dorling Kindersley: Chris Gomersall Photography (bc). 100 Dorling Kindersley: Roger Tidman (c). 101 Dorling Kindersley: Chris Gomersall Photography (c). 103 Getty Images: Steven Kazlowski (tl). 108 Dorling Kindersley: George McCarthy (bc)
Jacket images: Front: Corbis: Joe Petersburger / National Geographic Society c; Getty Images: Kevin Summers cla

All other images © Dorling Kindersley
For further information see: **www.dkimages.com**

a million voices for nature
The RSPB works for a healthy environment rich in birds and wildlife. Nature is amazing - help us keep it that way

Wildlife Explorers is the junior membership of the RSPB. To find out more and how to become a member visit **www.rspb.org.uk/youth**

If you would like to know more about the RSPB, visit the website at **www.rspb.org.uk** or write to: **RSPB**, The Lodge, Sandy, Bedfordshire, SG19 2DL. Tel. 01767 680551

The author, **Rob Hume,** has watched birds all his life. He worked for the RSPB for 35 years and now edits for them, as well as for other organizations. He also writes books to help other people learn about birds. This book is dedicated to his grandson, Noah Holt.